SUPER SOLVERS

There may be more than one way to solve a problem.

Copyright ' 1996 by Scholastic Inc.   All rights reserved.   Printed in the U.S.A.
ISBN 0-590-48807-4

5 6 7 8 9 10   23   02 01 00 99 98 97

Tour a
Toy Company

There may be more
than one way to solve
a problem.

Clever Ideas

Some problems need clever solutions.

Many Hands

We work together to solve problems.

Try, Try Again

It may take more than one try to solve a problem.

Trade Books

The following books accompany this *Super Solvers* SourceBook.

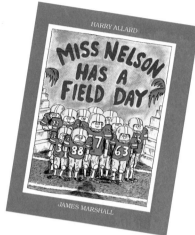

Humorous Fiction
Miss Nelson Has a Field Day
by Harry Allard
illustrated by James Marshall

AWARD WINNING — Illustrator

Popular Fiction
Pet Show!
by Ezra Jack Keats

AWARD WINNING — Book

Realistic Fiction
New Shoes for Silvia
by Johanna Hurwitz
illustrated by Jerry Pinkney

AWARD WINNING — Author/Illustrator

Big Book

West African Folk Tale
Zomo the Rabbit
by Gerald McDermott

AWARD WINNING — Book

Clever Ideas

Some problems need clever solutions.

Watch a boy solve the problem of having too many **aunts**.  Then join a child who's watching **ants** solve their anthill problems.

Be amazed at the way a paper crane helps  a restaurant owner with his business.

Meet a toy designer who knows what makes a good toy.

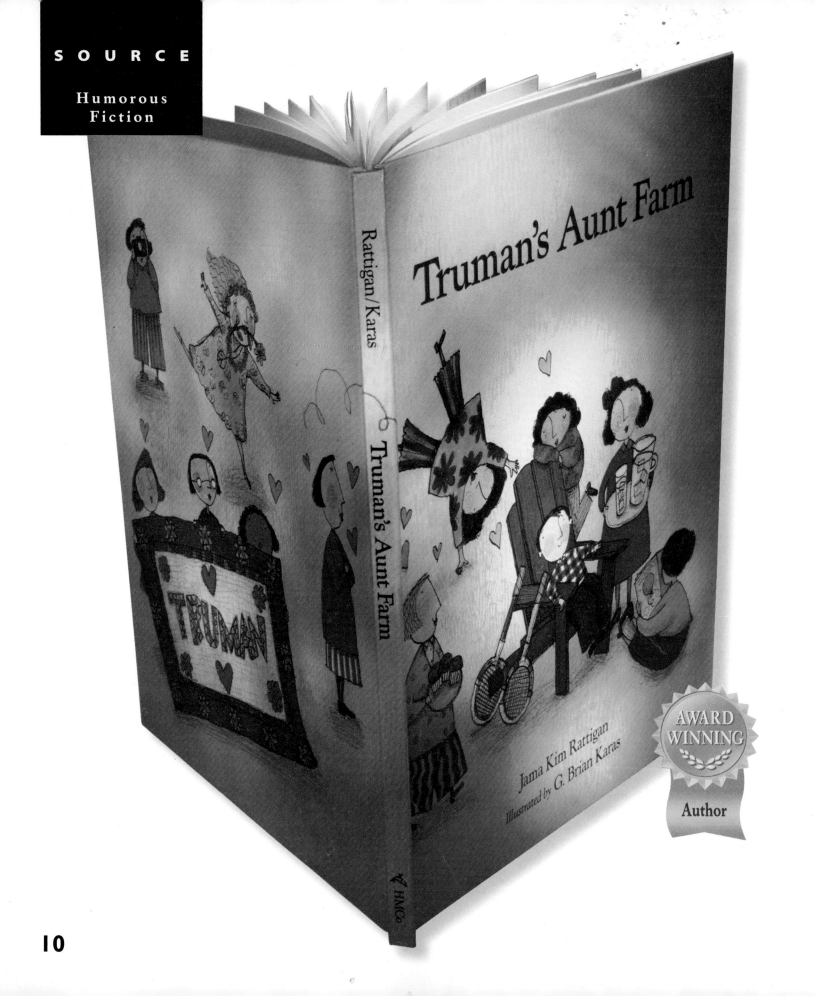

Truman's Aunt Farm

Rattigan/Karas

Truman's Aunt Farm

Jama Kim Rattigan

Illustrated by G. Brian Karas

AWARD WINNING

Author

HMCo

At eleven o'clock a package arrived for Truman. It was a birthday present from Aunt Fran. Truman looked at the box. It was not moving. He gently picked it up. It felt empty. He turned it over, then smelled it. Presents from Aunt Fran had to be handled very carefully.

Truman slowly opened the box. It was empty! No, there were two cards. The yellow one said: "Happy Birthday dear Truman! I am giving you the ant farm you wanted. Love, your charming Aunt Fran."

The green one said: "Mail this card right away to receive your free ants! Watch them work! Watch them play! Watch them eat! Live ants!"

Truman mailed his card right away. Oh boy. Live ants! Live ants for his very own!

But he didn't get ants. He got *aunts*.

13

It was true. There were aunts everywhere. They all loved
Truman and made such a fuss!

"My, how you've grown," said Aunt Lulu.

"Isn't he handsome?" said Aunt Jodie.

"Looks just like me," said Aunt Ramona. And they
hugged him, and patted his head, and pinched his cheeks,
and talked his ears off.

Dear Charming Aunt Fran,

Thank you for the birthday present.
I have fifty-something aunts at my house now.
More are arriving daily. What shall I do?

Love,
Your bug-loving nephew, Truman

P.S. What should I feed the aunts?

Truman looked out his front window. A long, long line of aunts was waiting to get in. They brought their knitting and homemade banana bread and gave Truman more than one hundred-something gift subscriptions to children's magazines.

"Help!" yelled Truman.

"Letter for you," said the postman.

My dear Truman,

I am glad you liked the present. Don't let those ants bug
you. Do you have any friends who would like some ants?

Love,
Your clever Aunt Fran

P.S. Feed the ants ant food.

Since they were *his* aunts he wanted them to be good aunts. What was the best aunt food? Not coffee, the aunts stayed up all night. Not alphabet soup, the aunts talked too much. Certainly not chocolate, the aunts kissed him all the time.

Daily Schedule

Morning:
9:00 Tickle Practice
10:00 Headstands
10:30 Roller Skating
11:00 Hug Relay

Afternoon:
1:00 Stories
2:00 Naps
3:00 Listening
5:00 Tiptoeing

So Truman fed them rice pudding for breakfast, jelly sandwiches for lunch, and little hot dogs for supper.

Every morning, all the aunts lined up for inspection. Truman walked up and down the ranks. He looked over each aunt from head to toe. They were ready to get to work.

The aunts got water and sun and fresh air. They blew bubbles, flew kites, and found birds' nests. Aunt Amy could do back flips with her eyes closed.

21

The aunts were strong and happy. They were charming and clever. They slept, played, sang, danced, and talked just enough.

Dear clever Aunt Fran,

I have around two hundred-something aunts now.
I love them all. More aunts keep coming and coming.
They are the best in the world.

Love,
Your aunt-loving nephew, Truman

Yes, they were very good aunts. But they weren't really *his* aunts. And he was running out of room. Could he give them away? Who might want them?

Truman put up a sign:

TRUMAN'S
AUNT
FARM

LIVE AUNTS!
WATCH THEM WORK!
WATCH THEM PLAY!
WATCH THEM EAT!
FREE TO GOOD HOMES

Truman looked out his front window. A long, long line of boys and girls was waiting to get in.

"I want a funny aunt," said one girl, "one who knows jokes and stories."

"I want my aunt to do cartwheels," said a little boy, "and not cry if she falls down and gets dirty."

"Make mine lumpy and soft. A good cuddler," said another boy.

Truman let all the boys and girls in. They looked over the aunts from head to toe. They watched the aunts work and play. They watched the aunts eat. The aunts could tickle, tell stories, do headstands, and roller skate. When the children talked, the aunts really listened. They didn't pat heads, pinch cheeks, or talk ears off. But they still hugged.

Soon, each child found just the right aunt.

"Goodbye, dear Truman!" called the aunts.
"Thanks for a tiptop time."
Truman was sad to see the aunts go. He watched them tiptoe away. He was glad those boys and girls got their own aunts, but something was missing.

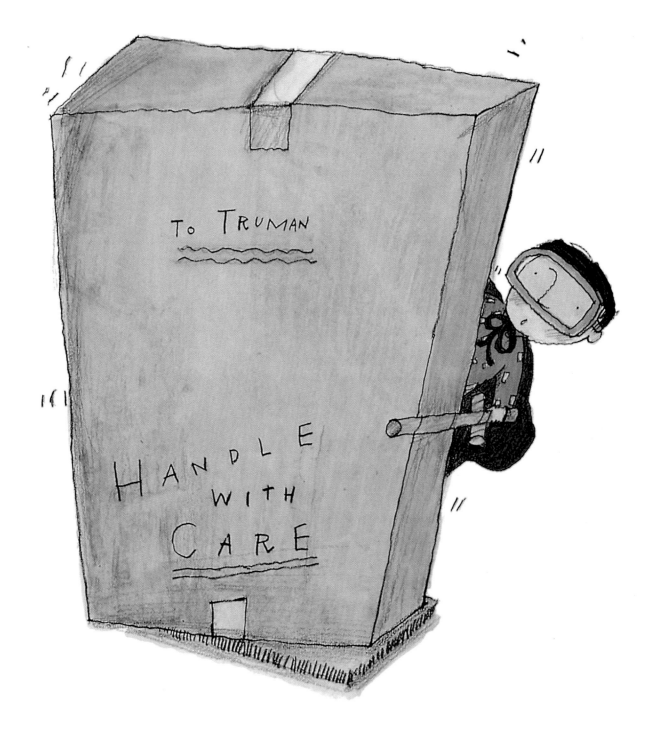

On the box: TO TRUMAN / HANDLE WITH CARE

At eleven o'clock the next day another package arrived. Truman looked at the box. It was moving. He tried to pick it up. It was too heavy. He smelled it. It smelled like roses. Carefully, he opened the lid.

Out jumped Aunt Fran!

"Surprise!" She gave Truman a big hug. "But where are your ants?" she said. "I wanted to see them."

"Oh, Aunt Fran! The aunts are gone. They have their own nieces and nephews now."

Aunt Fran put her arm around Truman. He saw the
twinkle in her eye. "You did a wonderful thing," said Aunt
Fran. "Let's celebrate your birthday."

Truman and his very own Aunt Fran shared a special day. They had rice pudding for breakfast, jelly sandwiches for lunch, and little hot dogs for supper. They even had a tickle contest, but they were too full to do headstands.

Ants

by Mary Ann Hoberman
illustrated by Lisa Adams

I like to watch the ants at work
When I am out at play.
I like to see them run about
And carry crumbs away.

And when I plug an anthill door
To keep them in their den,
I like to see them find a way
To get outside again.

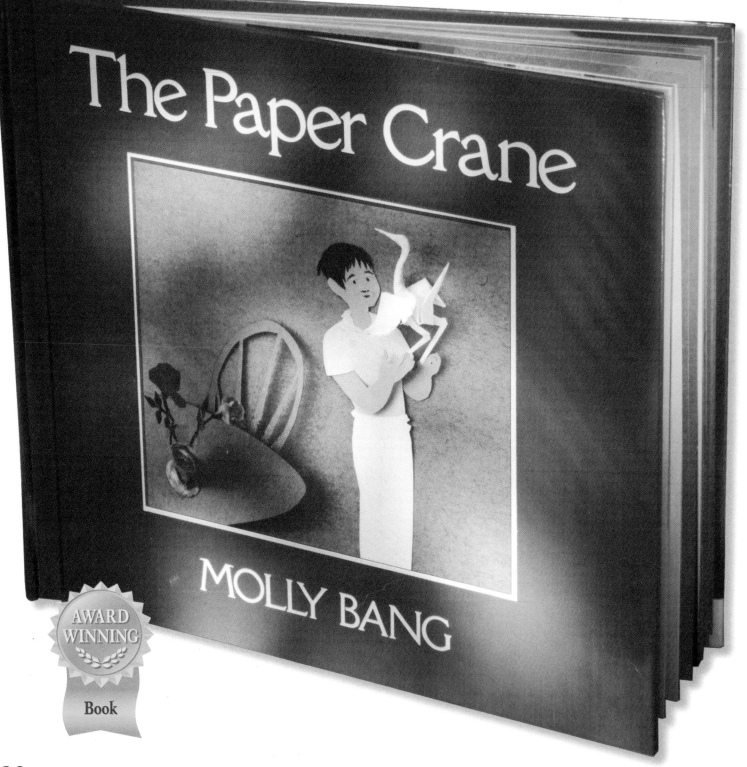

The Paper Crane

MOLLY BANG

A man once owned a restaurant on a busy road.
He loved to cook good food and he loved to serve it.
He worked from morning until night, and he was happy.

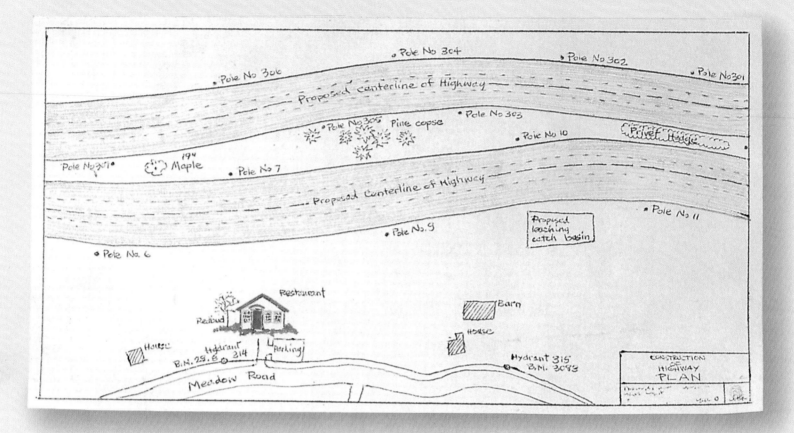

But a new highway was built close by. Travelers drove straight from one place to another and no longer stopped at the restaurant. Many days went by when no guests came at all. The man became very poor, and had nothing to do but dust and polish his empty plates and tables.

One evening a stranger came into the
restaurant. His clothes were old and worn,
but he had an unusual, gentle manner.

Though he said he had no money to pay for food, the owner invited him to sit down. He cooked the best meal he could make and served him like a king.

When the stranger had finished, he said to his host,
"I cannot pay you with money, but I would like to thank
you in my own way."

He picked up a paper napkin from the table and folded it into the shape of a crane. "You have only to clap your hands," he said, "and this bird will come to life and dance for you. Take it, and enjoy it while it is with you." With these words the stranger left.

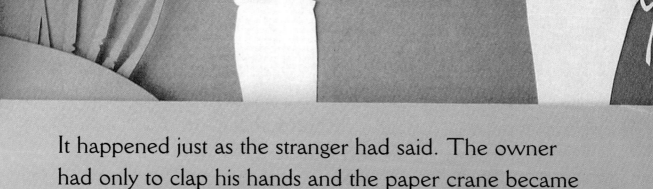

It happened just as the stranger had said. The owner
had only to clap his hands and the paper crane became
a living bird, flew down to the floor, and danced.

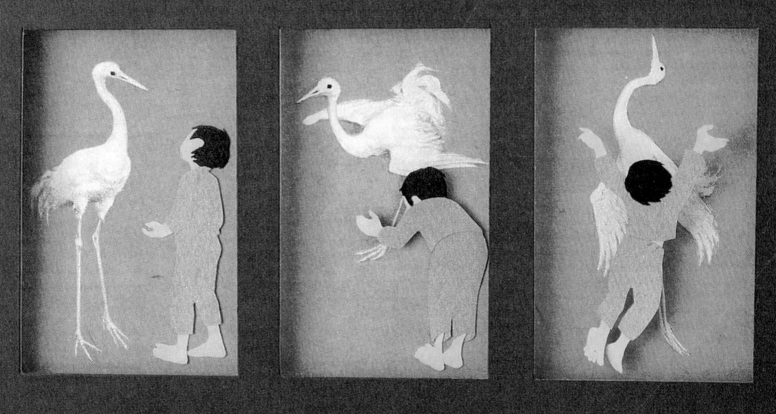

Soon word of the dancing crane spread, and people came from far and near to see the magic bird perform. The owner was happy again, for his restaurant was always full of guests.

44

He cooked and served and had company from morning until night.
The weeks passed.   And the months.

One evening a man came into the restaurant. His clothes
were old and worn, but he had an unusual, gentle manner.
The owner knew him at once and was overjoyed.

The stranger, however, said nothing. He took a flute from his pocket, raised it to his lips, and began to play.

The crane flew down from its place on the shelf and danced as it had never danced before. The stranger finished playing, lowered the flute from his lips, and returned it to his pocket. He climbed on the back of the crane, and they flew out of the door and away.

The restaurant still stands by the side of the road, and guests still come to eat the good food and hear the story of the gentle stranger and the magic crane made from a paper napkin. But neither the stranger nor the dancing crane has ever been seen again.

Mary Rodas

Toy Designer

A toy that's NOT fun?
That's a PROBLEM!

Some people just love problems! Finding and fixing problems are part of some people's jobs.

Mary Rodas is the vice president of Catco Inc., a toy company. When the company makes a toy, Rodas's job is to look at it and see if there is any problem. She works on the toy to make sure it's fun!

Questions

Here's how toy designer Mary Rodas solves problems on her job.

Q How did you get this job while you were still in school?

A When my neighbor Donald Spector started inventing toys, he would ask me what I thought of his new toy ideas. When he started his own toy company, he hired me to help him.

Q How do you decide if a toy might have a problem?

A First, a designer shows me a drawing of a new toy. Then, I look at a model of it. I try to think if the toy will be fun for children. If not, it should be changed.

54

Q **Have you solved a problem about a toy?**

A One day I was looking at a white ball called a Balzac Balloon Ball®. I thought the color wasn't exciting, so the designers made the ball in bright colors. Now the ball is a big hit!

®

®

Mary Rodas's Tips for Solving Problems

1 Be positive. Believe you can solve the problem.

2 Don't give up. Keep trying ways to find a solution.

3 If you need help, don't be afraid to ask for it.

Many Hands

We work together to solve problems.

Find out how a boy gets some very messy pigs to clean up.

Join a group of mice as they figure out how to save themselves from the cat. Then read the advice children give to other children.

57

Pigsty

by MARK TEAGUE

Teague

PIGSTY

Scholastic

AWARD WINNING

Book

onday afternoon Wendell Fultz's
mother told him to clean his room.
"It's turning into a pigsty," she said.

Wendell went upstairs. Much to his surprise,
a large pig was sitting on his bed.

"Pardon me," said Wendell. He shoved some toys
into his closet. But the pig didn't seem to mind
the mess, and Wendell found that he didn't mind
the pig, either.

He decided to take a break.

When Wendell's mother came to look at his room, the pig was hiding, but the mess was still there. She threw up her hands.

"Okay, Wendell," she said. "If you want to live in a pigsty, that's up to you."

Wendell could hardly believe his luck. "Now I can live however I want."

He didn't even worry when he came home on Tuesday and found a second pig in his room. The mess had grown a bit worse, but he was able to jam most of it under his bed.

"Pigs are all right," he said, "as long as it's only one or two."

In fact, they had a wonderful time. They played Monopoly
until late each night . . .

. . . and left the pieces lying all over the floor.

They had paper airplane wars and pillow fights.
The bed became a trampoline.

Then two more pigs showed up.
The mess just grew and grew.

That night when Wendell went to bed, the pigs were lying everywhere. They rolled up in his blankets and hogged his pillows, too.

Wendell told himself he didn't mind, but then he found hoofprints on his comic books.

And Friday when he got home from school, he saw
that someone had been sitting on his basketball.
And his baseball cards were chewed.

"That does it!" said Wendell. "I've had enough!"
He ran downstairs to tell his mother.

"Sorry," she said, "but your room is your
responsibility." She handed him a broom.

Wendell started to complain. The mess was too huge. But suddenly he remembered a saying he'd heard, that "many hooves make light work."

He marched upstairs and organized a cleaning crew.

They swept and scoured, polished and scrubbed.

Later that afternoon, Wendell inspected his room
and pronounced it "clean."

In fact, it was a bit too clean, from a pig's point of view. So while Wendell inspected, the pigs prepared to go home. One of them made a phone call, and a farm truck came to pick them up. They hugged and grunted and oinked "good-bye."

From that day on, Wendell kept his room clean . . .

. . . except for those nights
when his friends came by
to play Monopoly.

from

ONCE IN A WOOD
TEN TALES FROM AESOP

Adapted and illustrated by
Eve Rice

BELLING THE CAT

A hungry cat had come to stay
and all the mice lived in fear.
The mice decided
they would call a meeting.

When they were
all together,
the biggest mouse
stood up and said,
"There is a hungry cat about.
As long as he walks these woods,
not one of us is safe.
So I ask you all to think.
What are we to do?"
Then one mouse gave a plan.
And one mouse gave another.
And still a third had his say
and on and on until
a very young mouse spoke.

"Friends," he said.
"I think that we can
solve this problem easily:

82

Hang a bell on the cat.
Then we will know when he is near
and we can stay out of his way."

"A good idea!" someone called.
And all the other mice agreed.
"We'll be safe at last!" they said
and danced around until
a very old mouse spoke.

"Friends," he said.
"One moment, please.
Things are easier said than done—
the old and wise will tell you that.
So now, will someone tell me this:
Who is going to bell the cat?"

SOURCE

U•S• Kids

A *Weekly Reader*
Magazine

KIDS™

Helping Kids

Friends

Photos by Julie Bidwell
Illustration by Maja Anderson

Dear kids,
  I have a big problem.
I don't have any friends
at my new school. I
don't know what to say
to other kids, so most
of them think I'm stuck
up. When I try to join
them at recess, they
just walk away. No one
likes me, and I can't
stand it. What should
I do?
                Jessica B.
                Texas

W e asked our Kids Helping Kids panel about Jessica's letter. Here are the panel's ideas.

JESSE
Maybe the kids are a little shy around someone new. Maybe there's another new person at school you could get to know first.

ADAM
Keep asking to play. They will let you.

ANDREA

Ask yourself why you are so scared. You know that you're new there, and you can't expect to get to know kids right away.

MICHAEL

Find something to do by yourself, like jump rope. Someone may want to join you after all.

KA'LISHA

If they walk away from you, just let it go. Making friends takes time.

YEISSMAN

Joining a club will help you get to know other kids, and they'll get to know you, too.

87

When the Sitter JUST SITS

JESSE

You should talk to her and ask why she doesn't want to do anything fun. Maybe you could change the schedule to make time for things she'll enjoy doing with you. She may want to help with your homework if you ask her. Maybe you could ask the sitter to come up with ideas to help pass the time.

MICHAEL

Your mother is paying her to keep you company. If she doesn't, then tell your mother what's going on. I don't think she'll want to lose her job. Make the TV off-limits for everyone.

ANDREA

Maybe there are games she'd like to play if you ask her. Maybe you can go over to a friend's house to play or ride a bike. Or you can ask your parents for another sitter because this one just isn't interested in you.

ADAM

Ask your parents for permission to watch TV after your homework is done. Tell your parents that you want to watch your TV shows, not just the ones the sitter likes.

YEISSMAN

Talk to the sitter and tell her you want to do something fun. If that doesn't work, just keep trying. Tell her you're bored and you need something to do. Maybe your parents have some ideas to make the time more fun for both of you.

KA'LISHA

Find something to do on your own. You have rights, too. See if you can play with your friends when the sitter is there. Maybe you and the sitter can cook together.

Try, Try Again

It may take more than one try to solve a problem.

Break codes to read secret messages from the Code King. Then meet the man who created the art for this story.

Take notes with Martí as he tries to figure out what a mango is. See how many ways a chicken finds to share her fruit.

Scholastic 590-xxxxx-X

THE CODE KING

by Bill Dallas Lewis

SCHOLASTIC

It was a slow Saturday afternoon, and Rosa and Jimmy were sitting at the bus stop with nothing to do.

"I'm bored," Jimmy said.

"We could go to a movie," suggested Rosa.

The Main Street bus pulled up. Some people got on and the bus pulled away.

Just then, a paper airplane landed at Jimmy's feet. He picked it up and unfolded it. There was writing inside.

"What does that mean?" asked Jimmy.

"It must be a secret code," said Rosa.

Jimmy took a pencil from his pocket. Then he drew lines between some letters. "I've got it!" he said. "It's lots of words stuck together. In the park, under the slide, is a great place for a clue to hide!"

Rosa and Jimmy ran to the neighborhood park.
"There's the note," Jimmy yelled.
They studied the piece of paper.

"I like pizza with extra cheese, pepperoni, and
mushrooms, please. This is easy now," said Rosa.
"Maybe we can catch up with the Code King at Higgy's
Pizza Place!"

When Rosa and Jimmy got to Higgy's, they sat down at the counter and looked around.

Mrs. Higgy came up to them. "Hi, kids," she said, "someone left this note for you."

Rosa opened the note and looked at it.

"Hmmmmm," Jimmy said. "The Code King has changed his code."

"What if we zigzag the letters up and down?" asked Rosa. "Hand me that pencil, Jimmy."

Suddenly Rosa called out, "Fire. Fire. Save the day. Captain Rogers, two blocks away."

HELP THE MAN THEY CALL POP
HE HAS A LIST FOR YOU TO SHOP
THE CODE KING

Captain Rogers was polishing his fire engine when Jimmy and Rosa arrived at the fire station. "Hi," Jimmy said. "Did anyone leave a message for us?"

Captain Rogers pointed to the chalkboard and said, "Look there."

They looked at the message on the chalkboard for a long time. They were about to give up. Then Jimmy called out, "Rosa! Look at the reflection on the truck! Now the message makes sense. The words on the chalkboard were written backwards."

"They call my neighbor, Mr. Jones, Pop. I know where he lives. Follow me!" Jimmy said.

Jimmy and Rosa raced to Mr. Jones's house. Rosa knocked on the door.

"Hi. Here's the list," said Mr. Jones. He handed over a piece of paper and some money. "Thanks for doing my shopping," he said.

mushrooms
onions
vanilla
milk
large eggs
bananas

At the Sunflower Market, Jimmy and Rosa bought all the items on the list. Then they returned to see Mr. Jones.

"Here's your list back," Rosa said after handing over the groceries.

"Keep the list," said Mr. Jones. "There's a message on the back for you."

Rosa turned the paper over and read it.

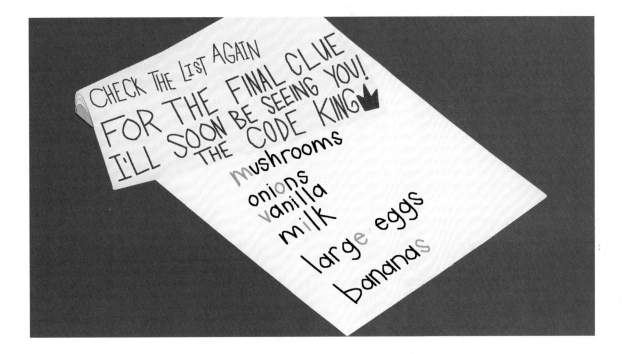

When Jimmy and Rosa looked at the shopping list this time, they noticed that each word had one letter in green. When they put the green letters together, they spelled "movies."

Outside the movie theater, Rosa said, "I don't see any Code King, do you?"

"No," Jimmy answered glumly. "And no more clues, either."

Rosa tugged Jimmy's sleeve. "There's your sister, Tina!"

Tina walked over and said, "Hi. I have three tickets for the next movie. Want to go?"

Jimmy asked, "How did you know we would be here?"

Tina smiled and said, "The Code King has her ways."

Secrets of THE CODE KING Artist: Bill Dallas Lewis

Why do you like to use the computer to draw?

"My computer's name is Henry. He is my second-best friend in the world. Using Henry, I can make big changes in my pictures. When you use crayons or watercolors, you can't do that. I can change day to night in a picture by pushing one button."

How do you make people on the computer?

"I use something special called a curve tool. I make a big circle for the head. I make little circles for the eyes. Then I make different curves for the mouth, nose, ears, arms, and legs. The curve tool is great for making hair too!"

How do you make the same person over and over again?

"Once I draw a person I save her in Henry's memory. When I need to use her again, I pull her up out of Henry's memory. If she needs to be bigger for the new picture, I can stretch her. I can bend her arms or change a smile to a frown."

Hi, my name is Henry.

107

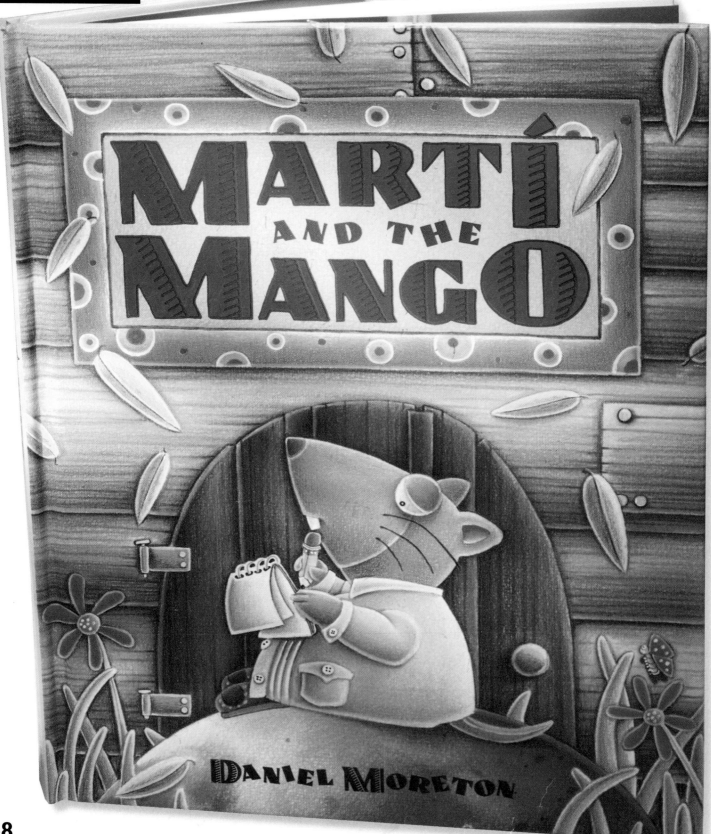

**M**artí lived on a small island, in a tiny house, at the base of a very tall tree.

**M**artí was a simple mouse, whose life consisted of simple pleasures: spending time with his best friend Gomez, afternoons in the sun, and a good imported Swiss cheese every now and again.

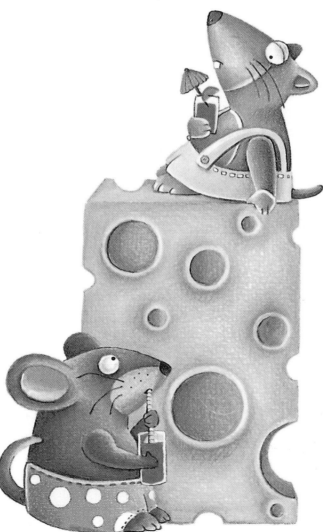

One day, however, Martí was faced with a rather extraordinary task.

He awoke as usual, and, as usual, he did his morning exercises. But when he went outside, he found a note from his friend Gomez tacked to the front of his door.

Dinner Tonight at my house. Bring a mango. —Gomez

"A mango?" thought Martí. "Who ever heard of such a thing? What does a mango look like?" he wondered. "And where on earth can I get one?"

Martí was a very curious mouse.

uickly, Martí put on his lucky shirt and headed out in search of this mysterious mango. First he decided to stop next door at the lily pond, where his neighbor Frog was on his way out.

"Excuse me," said Martí. "What's a mango?"

"A mango is a fruit!" Frog said, and—KERPLUNK— disappeared into the pond.

"Now we're getting somewhere," thought Martí. He took out his notebook and made a note that a mango is a fruit, and went on.

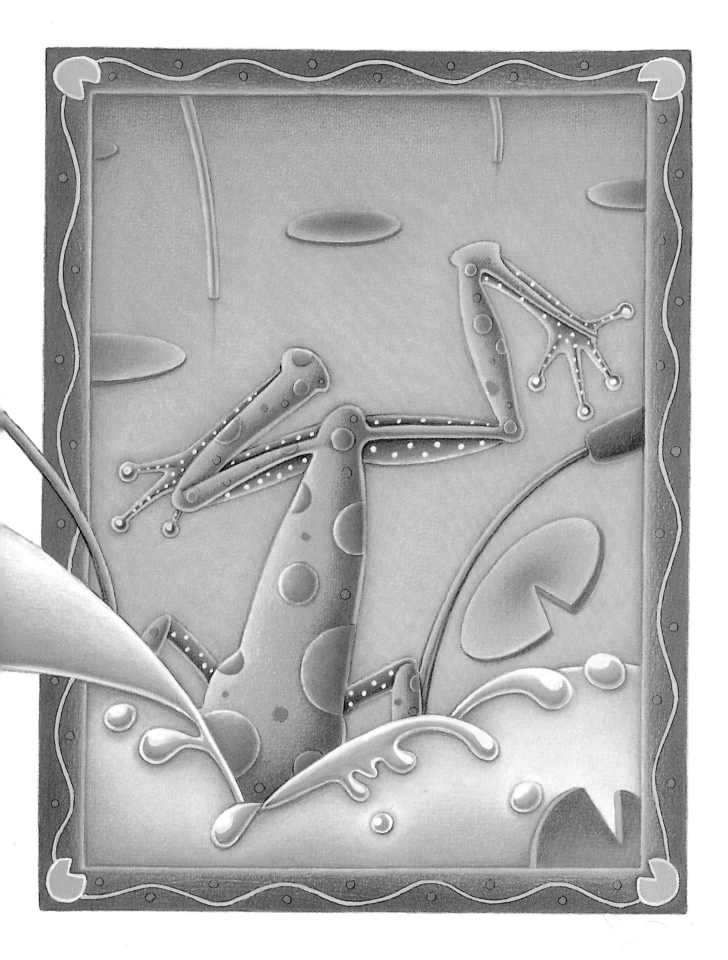

econd, Martí came across a gorilla gathering guavas.

"Excuse me," said Martí, "are those mangos?"

"Of course not," groaned the gorilla. "Mangos are much bigger. These are guavas."

"Thank you," said Martí. He made a note that a mango is a fruit bigger than a guava, and went on.

ext, he met a worm working her way through a watermelon.

"Excuse me," said Martí, "is that a mango?"

"Not to my knowledge," whispered the worm. "A mango is much smaller. This is a watermelon."

"Thank you," said Martí. He made a note that a mango is a fruit bigger than a guava, but smaller than a watermelon, and went on.

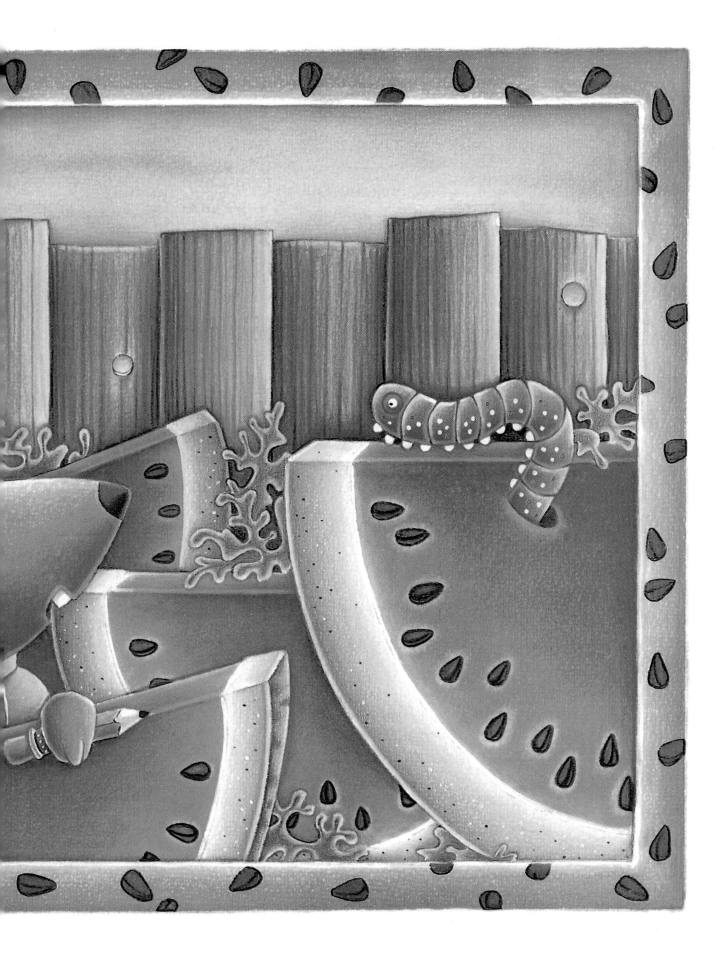

Soon after, Martí saw a kangaroo collecting kiwis.

"Excuse me," said Martí, "are those mangos?"

"Not at all," crooned the kangaroo. "Mangos are much smoother. These are kiwis."

"Thank you," said Martí. He made a note that a mango is a fruit bigger than a guava, but smaller than a watermelon, and smoother than a kiwi, and went on.

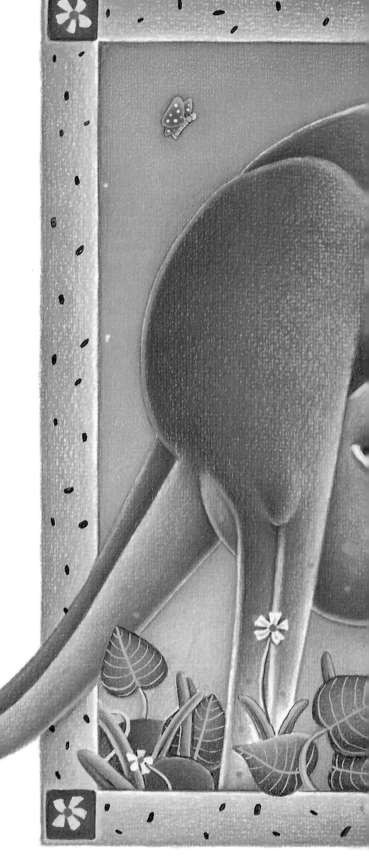

119

ater, Martí ran into some beavers bearing bananas.

"Excuse me," said Martí, "are those mangos?"

"No, no, no," babbled a beaver. "Mangos are much rounder. These are bananas."

"Thank you," said Martí. He made a note that a mango is a fruit bigger than a guava, but smaller than a watermelon, smoother than a kiwi, and rounder than a banana, and went on.

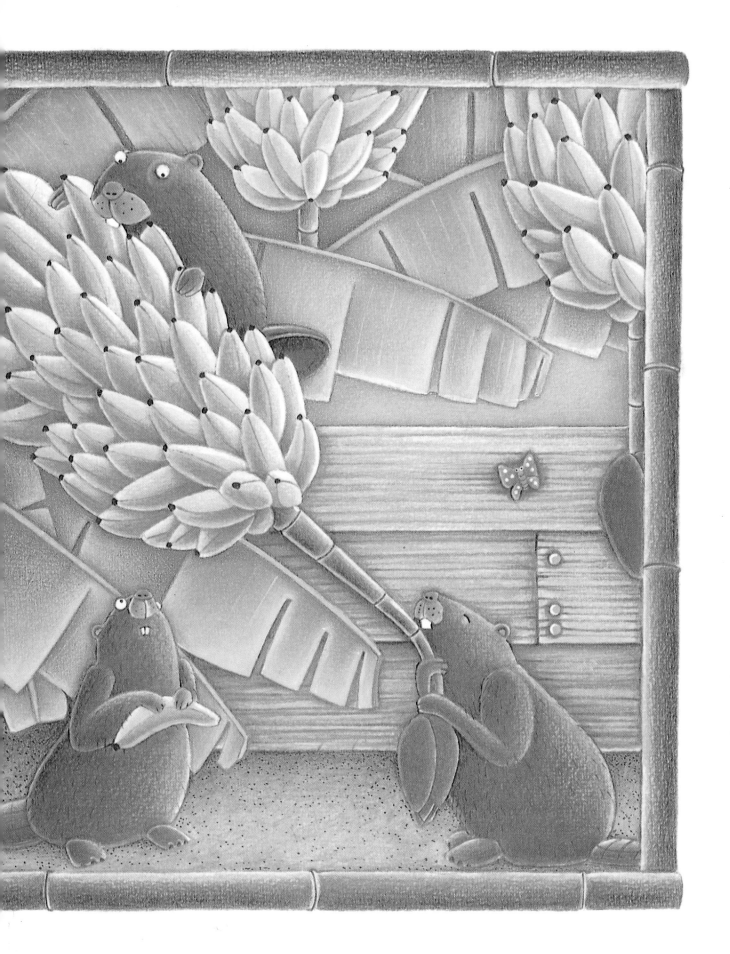

121

In the afternoon, Martí came upon a cockroach creeping across a coconut.

"Excuse me," said Martí, "is that a mango?"

"Hardly!" croaked the cockroach. "A mango is much softer. This is a coconut."

"Thank you," said Martí. He made a note that a mango is a fruit bigger than a guava, but smaller than a watermelon, smoother than a kiwi, rounder than a banana, and softer than a coconut, and went on.

hen he came to an alligator arranging some avocados.

"Excuse me," said Martí, "are those mangos?"

But the alligator did not answer. So Martí went on.

125

By now it was getting late, and Martí had become quite discouraged. He decided to head home without his mango. When he got there, he sat down, tired from his search.

"I'll never find this mango," said Martí unhappily. "I can't find anything. I can't go to Gomez's party without a mango. I'm a failure."

Martí was a very depressed mouse.

127

Just then Frog came bouncing by on a fig.
"I see you've found your mango," he said to Martí.

"Please don't tease me," begged Martí. "I have
not found my mango."

"But you're sitting right on
it!" bellowed Frog, and he
bounced off down the hill.

**arti looked down to see just what it was he was sitting on. "Could this be a mango?" he thought. He referred to his notes.**

a mango is a fruit

Bigger than a guava

Smaller than a Watermelon

Smoother than a kiwi

Rounder than a Banana

Softer than a Coconut

"This *is* a mango!" cheered Martí. And he smiled a very big smile.

Martí was a very happy mouse.

130

SOURCE

Cartoon

AWARD
WINNING

Author/
Illustrator

from Fraction Action

A Fair Share

by Loreen Leedy

One Saturday at about noon, Sadie heard a loud knock at the door.

132

133

135

Glossary

agreed
said yes
to something
The teacher **agreed**
to take us to the zoo
next week.

avocados
fruits shaped like
pears, but with green
or black skin and
yellow-green insides
Avocados can be
cut up in slices
for a salad.

avocado

cards
folded pieces of paper
with a greeting
for a special day
My sister got a lot of
cards on her birthday.

celebrate
to show happiness
by doing something
special
My family had a party
to **celebrate** my
brother's new job.

clothes
things that we wear
Jamal's favorite
clothes are a blue
T-shirt and jeans.

clue
something that helps
you solve a mystery
or know what
happened
The food on the
baby's face was a
clue that he had just
eaten lunch.

code
a secret way of
writing in which
letters or numbers
have a special
meaning
Tanya and her best
friend write notes
to each other in a
special **code**.

company
people in a group
Most people like **company** when they go on a trip.

decided
chose after thinking about something
The class **decided** to present a play to the whole school.

gift
something special given to someone
The bicycle was the best **gift** she had ever gotten.

guavas
yellow or green fruits often shaped like pears, with white or pink insides
Guavas can be used to make jelly.

guavas

guests
people who are visiting someone's home or staying at a hotel
Ryan and his brother are **guests** at our house for the holidays.

host
a person who greets people in a restaurant
The **host** seated the people at a table in the corner.

idea
a thought
I have an **idea** for something to do Saturday afternoon.

kiwis
small fruits shaped like eggs, with brown fuzzy skin and green insides
After we peeled the **kiwis**, we put them in the salad.

kiwis

mango
a fruit that has tough skin with a rosy tint and orange insides
A **mango** is a juicy fruit.

mango

message
news sent from one person to another
Denise sent a **message** to her friend Trisha.

package
a box with something in it
He opened the biggest **package** first.

pigsty
a messy, dirty place like a pen for pigs
If she doesn't clean her room soon, it will turn into a **pigsty**.

polished
made bright and shiny
Eric **polished** his shoes until they shined.

present
something given for a special reason
He brought a **present** to his friend's party.

restaurant
a place where people buy and eat meals
Pat and Dave ate dinner at that **restaurant**.

scoured
cleaned by rubbing with something rough
I **scoured** the pan with a pad to get it clean.

scrubbed
cleaned by rubbing hard
I **scrubbed** the bathtub with a soapy brush.

secret
something that is hidden or not known by many people
We had a **secret** that we never told anyone.

solve
to find the answer
Can you **solve** this puzzle?

stranger
someone you don't know
Don't go anywhere with a **stranger**.

surprise
something you don't know about before it happens
We jumped from our hiding places as a **surprise** when Uncle Joe walked in.

swept
cleaned with a broom
I **swept** all the broken pieces off the floor.

travelers
people who visit another place
The **travelers** are tired from their long trip.

watermelon
a large fruit with green skin and red insides
We cut the huge **watermelon** into thick slices.

wise
makes good decisions, knows a lot
Our grandmother is very **wise** about bringing up children.

zigzag
a line that looks like a Z or one Z after another
The football player ran a **zigzag** across the field.

watermelons

141

Authors and Illustrators

Molly Bang pages 32–51

When Molly Bang worked on *The Paper Crane*, she tried many ways of making the pictures until she found the best way. She cut out colored pieces of construction paper and glued them onto paper. It took her a whole year to make all the pictures! Some other books she has written and illustrated are *Ten, Nine, Eight* and *Yellow Ball*.

Loreen Leedy pages 132–137

Reading, writing, and art have been Loreen Leedy's three favorite things since she was a little girl. Working on picture books is the perfect job for her! Many of Leedy's books use funny animal characters to show all the steps in real-life events. *The Furry News* explains how a newspaper works. *The Great Trash Bash* tells how a town cleans up.

Daniel Moreton
pages 108–131

Daniel Moreton says that his character Martí isn't just any mouse. Martí is a Cuban mouse! He is named after a famous Cuban hero. Because the author's family comes from Cuba, he wanted some Cuban things in his first story. The book is filled with pictures that show what Cuba is like.

Mark Teague   pages 58–79

Mark Teague used to work in a bookstore. Looking at the children's books got him thinking about doing his own. Strange and funny things are always happening in books by Teague. In *The Trouble With the Johnsons*, a boy moves in with a family of alligators. In *Frog Medicine*, a boy's book report leads him to visit a doctor who is a frog!

Acknowledgments

Grateful acknowledgment is made to the following sources for permission to reprint from previously published material. The publisher has made diligent efforts to trace the ownership of all copyrighted material in this volume and believes that all necessary permissions have been secured. If any errors or omissions have inadvertently been made, proper corrections will gladly be made in future editions.

Cover: Bill Mayer.

Interior: "Truman's Aunt Farm" from TRUMAN'S AUNT FARM by Jama Kim Rattigan, illustrated by G. Brian Karas. Text copyright © 1994 by Jama Kim Rattigan. Illustrations copyright © 1994 by G. Brian Karas. Reprinted by permission of Houghton Mifflin Co. All rights reserved.

"Ants" from YELLOW BUTTER PURPLE JELLY RED JAM BLACK BREAD by Mary Ann Hoberman. Text copyright © 1981 by Mary Ann Hoberman. Published by Viking Press. Reprinted by permission of Gina Maccoby Literary Agency.

"The Paper Crane" from THE PAPER CRANE by Molly Bang. Copyright © 1985 by Molly Garrett Bang. Reprinted by permission of Greenwillow Books, a division of William Morrow & Company, Inc.

"Pigsty" from PIGSTY by Mark Teague. Copyright © 1994 by Mark Teague. Reprinted by permission of Scholastic Inc. MONOPOLY® is a registered trademark of Tonka Corporation for its real estate trading game and elements. Copyright © 1934, 1992 Parker Brothers, a division of Tonka Corporation. Used with permission.

"Belling the Cat" and cover from ONCE IN A WOOD, adapted and illustrated by Eve Rice. Copyright © 1979 by Eve Rice. Reprinted by permission of Greenwillow Books, a division of William Morrow & Company, Inc.

"Kids Helping Kids: Friends" (September 1992) and "Kids Helping Kids: When the Sitter Just Sits" (January/February 1993) from *U*S*Kids®*, a *Weekly Reader* magazine. Copyright © 1992 by Children's Better Health Institute, Benjamin Franklin Literary & Medical Society, Inc. Indianapolis, IN. Reprinted by permission.

THE CODE KING by Bill Dallas Lewis. Copyright © 1996 by Scholastic Inc.

"Martí and the Mango" from MARTI AND THE MANGO by Daniel Moreton. Copyright © 1993 by Daniel Moreton. Reprinted by permission of Stewart, Tabori & Chang, Publishers, NY.

"A Fair Share" and cover from FRACTION ACTION by Loreen Leedy. Copyright © 1994 by Loreen Leedy. All rights reserved. Reprinted by permission of Holiday House, Inc.

Cover from MISS NELSON HAS A FIELD DAY by Harry Allard, illustrated by James Marshall. Illustration copyright © 1985 by James Marshall. Published by Houghton Mifflin Company.

Cover from NEW SHOES FOR SILVIA by Johanna Hurwitz, illustrated by Jerry Pinkney. Illustration copyright © 1993 by Jerry Pinkney. Published by William Morrow & Company, Inc.

Cover from PET SHOW by Ezra Jack Keats. Illustration copyright © 1972 by Ezra Jack Keats. Published by Aladdin Books, Simon & Schuster Children's Publishing Division.

Cover from ZOMO THE RABBIT: A TRICKSTER TALE FROM WEST AFRICA by Gerald McDermott. Illustration copyright © 1992 by Gerald McDermott. Published by Harcourt Brace Jovanovich, Publishers.

Photography and Illustration Credits

Selection Opener Photographs by David S. Waitz Photography/Alleycat Design, Inc. for Scholastic Inc.

Photos: pp. 2-3 c: © James Lukoski for Scholastic Inc. p. 3 br: © James Lukoski for Scholastic Inc. p. 52 tr: © John Lei for Scholastic Inc. p. 52 bl, cl: © James Lukoski for Scholastic Inc. p. 53 c, tr: © John Lei for Scholastic Inc. p. 54 br, cl: © John Lei for Scholastic Inc. tr: © John Bessler for Scholastic Inc. p. 55 c: © James Lukoski for Scholastic Inc.; tr: © John Lei for Scholastic Inc. pp. 86-89: © Julie Bidwell. p. 107 cr: © Mark Lyons for Scholastic Inc. p. 138 bl: © Stan Sholik/FPG International Corp. p. 139 br: © Eduardo Garcia/FPG International Corp.; tc: © Ray Coleman/Photo Researchers, Inc. p. 140 cl: © Photo Researchers, Inc. p. 141 bc: © R. Pleasant/FPG International Corp. p. 142 br: © Holiday House; bl: © Courtesy of William Morrow & Company. p. 143 br: Courtesy of Scholastic Trade Department, bl: Courtesy of Daniel Moreton

Illustrations: pp. 2-3: Jackie Snider; pp. 8-9: Dave Jolly; p. 31: Lisa Adams; pp. 56-57: Dave Jolly; pp. 80-85: Drew Brook-Cormack; pp. 90-91: Dave Jolly.